The Forgetful Puppy

This is a story about a real live Scottish Terrier called Izzy and her real-life pals and their adventures.

This story took place on October 28th and concerned a stick.

written & illustrated by Nigel Standerline

Pegasus

Pegasus PAPERBACK

© Copyright 2021
Nigel Standerline

A CIP catalogue record for this title is
available from the British Library.
ISBN 978-1-91090-378-0

Pegasus is an imprint of
Pegasus Elliot MacKenzie Publishers Ltd.
www.pegasuspublishers.com

First Published in 2021

Pegasus
Sheraton House Castle Park
Cambridge England

Printed & Bound in Great Britain

Thanks to

Izzy – the Scottie
Bailey – the Golden-doodle
Cornelius – the Wheaten Scottie
My wife Julie – the critic
Daughter Emma – also the critic
Ken Coton – the editor
Jaqui, Simon & Daisy – the encouragers

To Izzy and all who love her

Izzy was looking for a stick. She wanted a nice long one but not too thick.

Then, by the little stream in the mud, she saw the perfect stick.

She grabbed it with her strong white teeth and pulled. But the stick was stuck. So she pulled extra hard and fell over backwards as it squelched free.

seven

eight

Izzy jumped on to her four furry paws and picked up her stick at one end then walked off down the path past the vegetable garden.

She was proud of her special stick but the stick was naughty and got caught on everything Izzy walked past. So she put it down and grabbed it in the middle.

nine

Then she saw, through a gap in the hedge at the bottom of her garden, two dogs playing in the field beyond.

She ran off to join them at full speed and headed straight for the gap in the hedge, but she had forgotten about the stick held in her mouth. She suddenly stopped. Only her nose had gone through the hedge gap. The stick was too wide and it was now stuck in the leaves and twigs of the hedge.

ten

Izzy let go of the stick, pushed through the hedge and chased after her two playful puppy pals.

eleven

twelve

When Izzy caught up with her two friends Bailey and Cornelius, they were standing beside the little stream.

Bailey loved to swim and at the sight of the clear water he dived straight in, even though it was a cold autumn day.

The stream was deep and fast flowing, and Cornelius and Izzy had to run along the bank at quite a speed to keep level with him as the current carried him along.

thirteen

Suddenly a floating log drifted past and became tangled in Bailey's fur.

Then a supermarket shopping bag that was swirling in the water current joined them by catching on the log.

Then all three things stopped floating down the stream.

Something under the water had also caught in Bailey's fur.

Izzy and Cornelius also stopped and looked at each other surprised and concerned.

fourteen

fifteen

Izzy's immediate thought was 'Bailey is stuck, I need my stick to help him but where is it?' She had forgotten. Suddenly she remembered and ran off leaving Cornelius a little puzzled.

When she got back to where she had left the stick, the stick was *gone*!

Looking about she spotted it. Her special stick was stuck in the vegetable garden with a small brown flag tied to the top. Someone must have found it and thought 'there's a useful stick'.

sixteen

With no time to lose she ran at top speed, grabbed *her* stick, turned and raced back to help Bailey.

seventeen

When she got back to the stream, Izzy realised that Cornelius had jumped into the stream and dragged Bailey on to dry land (they were both now covered in slimy waterweed).

Bailey and Cornelius then realised that Izzy had not run away, she had rushed off to get her stick to help pull Bailey out of the stream.

After a few moments just looking at each other in silence, all three dogs started a game with Izzy's stick that lasted until they were called home.

eighteen

What a day it had been!

nineteen

The
end
...of
this
story

Now it's your turn to be creative.

have
FUN

Colouring suggestion - try adding extra stuff in the sky - birds, airplanes, UFO, balloons, flying granny, etc.

twenty-two

Colouring suggestion - shadows and reflections can make a 2 dimensional picture look like 3 dimensions.

Colouring suggestion – in October the leaves have fallen to the ground and the sun is thin and weaker than in summer months.

twenty-four

Colouring suggestion – when you look through glass windows the colour of things on the other side will often look lighter.

twenty-five

Colouring suggestion – try using texture to show the difference between areas of the picture. Everything has texture including Izzy.

twenty-six

Colouring suggestion – if you have lots of coloured pencils or pens, try making Izzy a different colour – perhaps pink!

twenty-seven

do not forget
there are other

Forgetful Puppy stories
coming soon

concerning a friend
concerning snow
concerning weight
concerning squirrels
concerning paint
concerning buried treasure
concerning a bath
concerning birthdays
concerning the car
concerning a bang
concerning a smell

Printed in Great Britain
by Amazon